Bunnykins
ABC

Ernest Benn
LONDON

The rabbit characters from which the now traditional
"Bunnykins" ® image evolved were created by an English
nun. Royal Doulton discovered her pencil drawings
in the 1930s and transformed them into the colourful
tableware and figures that have delighted
generations of children ever since.

Royal Doulton's own artists have continued the theme
and today designer Walter Hayward is responsible for
creating new scenes, each telling its own story with
an ageless charm and artistry, for use on their range
of gift pottery cherished by children the world over.

First published in 1982 by Ernest Benn Limited
25 New Street Square, London EC4A 3JA
© Ernest Benn Ltd. 1982

Illustrations © Royal Doulton Tableware Limited 1982
"Bunnykins" ® is a registered trade mark of Doulton & Co. Ltd.

Printed in Italy by La Editoriale Libraria, Trieste

ISBN 0 510 00108-4

A
Apple picking in autumn

B

Busy baking buns

C
Chopping carefully
for the campfire

D

Decorating disaster!

E

Eating Easter eggs

F
Fishing with father

G

Gardening with grandpa

H

Hiking over the high hill

I

I want an ice cream

J

Join in the jolly jig

K
Keep hold of your kite!

L

Last over the line

M
Making a mess at the market

N

Nice noises nearby

O

Over the ocean

P

Painting a portrait

Q

Quiet! No quacking in the queue!

R
Ring-a-ring o'roses

S
Snipping and sewing

T

Travelling on a train

U
Under our umbrellas

V

Violets for the vase

W

Washing, wiping, and
very wet!

X

Xmas and a xylophone!

Y

Yawning all in yellow

Z

Zooming down a zig-zag